5 FROGS®

TRANSFORMATION JOURNAL

REFLECTIONS ON THE ROAD TO RESILIENCE

STATION
SQUARE
MEDIA
NEW YORK, NEW YORK

5 FROGS® Transformation Journal
Reflections On the Road to Resilience

Published by Station Square Media
115 East 23rd Street, 3rd Floor
New York, NY 10010
www.stationsquaremedia.com

Editorial: Write to Sell Your Book, LLC
Interior Design: Steven Plummer, SP Design
Cover Design: Klassic Designs

Printed in the United States of America for Worldwide Distribution

ISBN: 978-0-9992268-7-2 (Hardcover)
ISBN: 978-0-9992268-8-9 (Spiral-bound)

First Edition
10 9 8 7 6 5 4 3 2 1

THIS TRANSFORMATION STORY BELONGS TO:

....

If this journal is found, and I'm not around (check one of the boxes):

☐ Please honor my privacy.

☐ Enjoy my journey and the wisdom contained here—
happy reading!

WHAT'S INSIDE

BEFORE YOU TAKE THE LEAP

BEHIND EVERY *NOW WHAT?* IS A *WHY NOT?!*
READY TO BE UNLEASHED.

A NOTE FROM BRENDA

I'VE BEEN JOURNALING from the time I was a young girl. My journal always felt like a not-so-faraway land that I could visit, leave my raw feelings on its beaches, and return home with a clearer head and a lighter heart. It was a land of no judgment—just a place for my truth. I don't journal consistently or with any pattern necessarily. But if I'm going through a spell of active journaling, I'm likely in the uncomfortable process of some transformation in my life. My frantic journaling is often a pre-cursor for growth that I can't see (yet).

We all imagine each other's lives sailing along swimmingly. Why is that? Because that's not true nor even possible for a human being. We may know people whom we admire for their resilience, but they didn't get there without being tossed among the waves or falling overboard a time or two. That's when it becomes imperative to know how to swim.

This journal is for you. It's a place to tread water and show up for yourself. It's a companion as you navigate land and sea on the road to your own growing resilience. It's a place for exploring the raw parts of your journey as well as the celebrations. It's a place where tears and inspiration can co-exist.

Between the covers of this journal, you can keep it real. There's no need to sugarcoat anything, write what you truly feel. Journaling is about telling the truth about what it means to be alive. It's a tool for transforming pain, sorrow, and bitterness into beauty. And in that transforming, we transform ourselves.

Pain feels like a detour from the main road, but it's actually part of the main road. When you show up for yourself here, you place yourself on the road to resilience. And just wait to see who you become!

WHY 5 FROGS®?

T HE TITLE OF this book grew from a transformation—in my life *and in the concept.* It started when my divorce attorney slid a box of tissues across the conference room table toward my snot-covered face with one declaration: "During this process, don't even think about coming in here and telling me about any prince you've met until you've kissed at least 5 frogs."

To this day it seems like such an odd, misplaced statement. At that time, I couldn't imagine ever dating again, never mind having 5 dates that involved kissing! So, I noted that odd piece of advice (which he has no recall of ever saying) and went on with my transformation.

When I began dating again, I thought of each man as a frog. Perhaps I'd write a book about that, I thought. Until I hit frog 5 and determined that no one would ever want to read that dull book!

But some part of me knew that I was supposed to do something with this 5 frogs concept because frogs began to show up everywhere.

One night I dreamed about a frog—a big frog wearing a small crown.

The next day a friend invited me to go shopping in a quaint little up-and-coming town nearby. We stumbled into a gift shop with merchandise overflowing the shelves as high as the eye could see. I walked through the door, glanced to my right and met the gaze of a small crown-adorned ceramic frog identical to the frog I had met in my dream the night before.

I kid you not. It was *identical.* The ceramic frog came home with me and has sat on my desk for quite some time as a reminder of this mission I had yet to figure out.

That same week I was cleaning out my office and found an old Christmas card from an environmental engineering client. Staring back at me was the exact same image of my newfound frog friend. *Really?*

Sometime later I was walking past the TV in my family room and heard someone saying that FROG was an acronym for Fully Reliant on God. Again, I tucked that one far back in the recesses of my mind, because I wasn't sure there even was a God at work in my life at that moment.

As time went by, I realized that during my life-gone-sideways divorce I had lived a different FROGS acronym of my own, made up of 5 stages and some major transformation.

> **F**: FREAKING OUT. Life as I'd known it had fallen apart. I was at a fork-in-the-road. I was freaking out and wanted it to fall back together asap.

> **R**: REFLECTING AND RESPONSIBILITY. As I took on new responsibilities as a single mom and provider, I reflected on one key question—*now what?* How was I going to manage this disorienting event, what was my responsibility in getting here, and what choices would I need to make now?

> **O**: Over time, I was slowly but surely OVERCOMING OBSTACLES.

> **G**: GROWING. Despite myself and my circumstances, I was GROWING—in small and big ways.

> **S**: SOVEREIGN SELF. And here's the thing—none of the growth had to do with a prince. There was no magical kiss or crown— just me, crowning a royal, more resilient version of myself—a stronger, evolved, expanded, transformed version of myself.

Before I started working on this journal, my knowledge of frogs was limited to Kermit and the kind that got kissed on the way to finding a prince. But when frogs kept showing up in my life, I thought it was time to learn more.

Here's what I discovered and reflected on about my new-found friends and why they are the perfect symbol of the transformations we all go through:

- Frogs are a symbol of change and transition.

- As frogs evolve from tadpoles to frogs, they literally lose their tails. They too suffer loss as part of their evolution.

- Many frogs are at risk of extinction. Like them, we evolve or die.

- They are also symbols of spiritual and emotional transformation. Could this be the outcome of your *"now what?"*

HOW TO USE THIS JOURNAL

Frogs are adaptable. They live on land and sea. But sometimes, their flippered, rubbery feet are firmly planted in mid-air as they navigate between the two spaces. Like them, sometimes we can feel the earth solidly under our feet; other times we're treading water. That's why this journal is set up differently than most.

We don't neatly cycle through the 5 FROGS stages. We may experience them simultaneously. And some days we relate more to one stage over the others. And our moods may experience frenetic swings. So, while this journal is organized according to the 5 stages, whichever space or mood you're in will dictate which section to make your entry in.

I guess it's frog-like that way—hopping from space to space.

But it makes looking back on the journey someday much easier. The final section of the journal gives you space to pause mid-air in the journey to summarize your observations along the way. We call them hops.

This 5 FROGS journal will contain thought-provoking prompts (jumpstarts), lily pads for reflection, inspirational quotes, and plenty of space for your emotions to land safely and your transformation story to unfold. It's a place to navigate your unique uncertainty on the road to becoming a more expanded, resilient version of yourself.

Resilience defined:

1. the capacity to recover quickly from difficulties; toughness.

2. the ability of a substance or object to spring back into shape; elasticity.

I've learned that resilience isn't a fixed trait. It isn't that some of us have it and some don't. It just requires a willingness to face our disorienting life events head on.

When you find yourself thinking "there's no way I'll come back from this," remember that you will.

Your resilience journey starts now—and here!

Hop to it!

"HOPE IS NOT BLIND OPTIMISM. FULLY ABSORB THE TRAGEDY OF YOUR MOMENT. ONLY AFTER YOU'VE ABSORBED THAT PAIN OR HARDSHIP, CAN YOU INSIST YOU WILL PREVAIL. THEN THERE'S A DEPTH TO YOUR HOPE. PROGRESS ISN'T A STRAIGHT LINE. IT ZIGS AND ZAGS."

— BARACK OBAMA ON LEADERSHIP
DARE TO LEAD PODCAST INTERVIEW WITH BRENE BROWN

FREAKING OUT

WHEN NOTHING IS SURE, EVERYTHING IS POSSIBLE.

W HAT THE F---! (frog, of course) *What* just happened?! A disorienting life event has come your way. Some part of life as you knew it has gone sideways. Or you've chosen to embark on some big change. Either way, you find yourself at a fork-in-the-road and asking yourself *now what?* Perhaps things are falling apart or away, and at best, you have your feet firmly planted in midair. You crave certainty but it evades you. It's like a big fog has just rolled in over your perfect life plan.

Are you floundering?

Feeling frustrated?

Freaking out?

Are your feelings fluctuating daily, hourly? One moment you're sad, the next you're angry. Perhaps you're scared. Nonetheless, it helps to vent these feelings. But who would you want to subject to this roller coaster ride of raw emotions?

This section of the 5 Frogs® Transformation Journal is meant to be a safe place to let your emotions fly! Writing them down may be the outlet you need for releasing them. Writing them out may help you clarify what's really going on for you and get to the root of an issue.

Regardless, these judgment-free pages are a place to unleash all the F-words you want!

JUMPSTART!

Not sure where to begin? Choose a prompt from below to jumpstart your F-stage writing. Find you have more to say? Open to a blank page and keep on writing.

What raw emotions do you need to unleash on these pages right now?

_____

_____

_____

_____

_____

What currently has you freaking out? What's keeping you up at night?

_____

_____

_____

_____

_____

What's the worst thing that could happen?

_____

_____

_____

_____

What helps you release your freak-out energy? (punching pillows, a good run, howling at the moon, crying it out).

....

....

....

....

What will you give yourself permission to do guilt-free?

....

....

....

....

How do you look after yourself after a bad day or moment?

....

....

....

....

....

What's your favorite curse word? Write it big and bold right here... permission granted.

....

Whose voice is echoing in your head and talking to you in critical ways? (it may be yours). What do you want to say back to it?

....

....

....

....

....

You've survived 100% of your worst days. What got you through them? How might you apply that now?

....

....

....

....

....

Give yourself permission to feel hard things; the world conspires against our difficult emotions—it says we should be happy. Sometimes the most courageous thing we can do is feel our feelings. What courageous version of freaking out do you need to allow yourself?

....

....

....

....

....

....

What are you being called to let go of? A person, a thing, a dream, a belief? Describe how that feels.

....
....
....
....
....
....
....

What do you need from each member of your circle of support army? Write about it specifically and consider sharing your needs with each person.

....
....
....
....
....

KEEP ON WRITING...

I WALK
AROUND LIKE
EVERYTHING'S FINE,
BUT DEEP DOWN, INSIDE
MY SHOE, MY SOCK
IS SLIDING OFF.

ANONYMOUS

FAILURE IS
JUST ANOTHER
NAME FOR MUCH
OF REAL LIFE.

MARGARET ATWOOD

IN THE DARKEST, MOST CHAOTIC TIMES—WHEN THINGS FALL APART— SUCH TIMES OFTEN MARK A QUICKENING AS YOUR MIND READIES ITSELF TO MAKE A LEAP. WHEN YOU FEEL LIKE YOU'RE GOING NOWHERE, STAGNATING, EVEN SLIPPING BACKWARD— YOUR SOUL IS ONLY BACKING UP TO GET A RUNNING START.

FROM *SACRED JOURNEY OF THE PEACEFUL WARRIOR* DAN MILLMAN

5 FROGS
F-STAGE WORDSEARCH

T	U	O	L	L	A	F	L	I	A	F	D
D	H	D	F	E	E	L	I	N	G	S	F
F	O	G	F	L	I	P	O	U	T	N	R
A	R	U	A	U	G	H	U	T	F	T	U
U	E	E	L	O	G	H	R	A	H	Z	S
R	R	N	A	E	R	U	L	I	A	F	T
A	S	U	O	K	U	L	U	E	X	U	R
E	L	L	X	G	O	G	N	F	Y	A	A
F	A	T	T	U	H	U	Q	O	P	T	T
G	U	T	T	E	T	H	T	U	A	L	E
F	O	R	K	I	N	R	O	A	D	A	D
D	E	C	R	H	G	U	A	H	C	K	E

FOG	FRUSTRATED	FEAR	FREAK OUT
FALLOUT	FEELINGS	FORK IN ROAD	FLIP OUT
FAILURE			

What are three positive feelings you'd like to be experiencing on the other side of your transformation?

_____, _____, _____.

EXPECTING
THE WORLD TO
TREAT YOU FAIRLY
BECAUSE YOU ARE GOOD
IS LIKE EXPECTING THE BULL
NOT TO CHARGE BECAUSE
YOU ARE A VEGETARIAN.

DENNIS WHOLEY

5 FROGS

ONLY
WHEN WE ARE
BRAVE ENOUGH
TO EXPLORE THE
DARKNESS WILL WE
DISCOVER THE INFINITE
POWER OF OUR LIGHT.

BRENÉ BROWN

**IF LIFE
WERE EASY, IT
WOULDN'T
BE DIFFICULT.**

KERMIT THE FROG

EVERYTHING
YOU WANT IS
ON THE OTHER
SIDE OF FEAR.

JOHN ADDAIR

LILY PAD

A group of frogs is called an army. You may feel like you are part of a war during this time. So, call in your support! Who's in your army? Who are the non-judgmental supporters, diplomatic truth tellers, who represent a circle of strength to you and support you unconditionally?

List them here.

1. ....

2. ....

3. ....

4. ....

5. ....

KEEP ON WRITING...

RESPONSIBILITIES
AND REFLECTION

REFRAMING IS THE MUSCLE TO BUILD WHEN YOU FEEL BURDENED WITH RESPONSIBILITY.

THIS IS THE stage where we recognize that things are different. A lot of responsibilities, pre-existing or new, will be piling up as you navigate this uncertain time. During this de-stabilizing time, you'll be highly distracted and prompted to act. But you want to ensure any actions you take are the result of clear thinking and intentional choice.

In the R stage, we pause to make room for awareness of what is unfolding, whether you like what is happening or not, whether it is pleasant or not.

We wrestle our attention down and reflect to stabilize our minds so that we can see what we need to see. If we tried to look at the moon, but set our telescope up on a waterbed, it would be hopeless to find the moon, keep it in view or study it carefully. So, in this stage, we pause to get on steady ground.

JUMPSTART!

Not sure where to begin? Choose a prompt from below to jump-start your R-stage writing. Find you have more to say? Open to a blank page and keep on writing.

What personal responsibility do you need to claim in getting to this disorienting situation? What was your part in it?

Who do you want to blame for getting you here? Go ahead, blame them and curse them on these pages. Then, let it go and focus on what's in your control and what's next.

What are the "big rocks" and additional weight you're carrying?

What new responsibilities are coming your way as a result of this change?

....

....

....

How are you feeling about having to be so darned responsible or taking on these new responsibilities?

....

....

....

What responsibilities rightfully belong to you? What responsibilities actually belong (or should belong) to others? Who else can help you take some of the responsibilities off your shoulders? (even temporarily)

....

....

....

What does self-care look like for you?

....

....

....

What self-care do you need to make time for right now?

....

....

....

Michelle Obama famously said, "When they go low, we go high." How might you need to put this phrase into practice right now?

....

....

....

What are the extreme negative thoughts in your head saying about you or to you? What do you want to say back? What story do you want to replace them with? What do you most need or want right now?

....

....

....

As you start to reflect, what early learning is already emerging?

....

....

....

Reflect and Remember: List 3 of your attributes that make you uniquely qualified to meet this challenge.

1. _____

2. _____

3. _____

KEEP ON WRITING...

"RESPONSIBILITY
FINDS A WAY.
IRRESPONSIBILITY
FINDS EXCUSES."

GENE BEDLEY

> ## "WITHOUT REFLECTION, WE GO BLINDLY ON OUR WAY."
>
> MARGARET J. WHEATLEY

"BETWEEN
STIMULUS AND
RESPONSE THERE IS A
SPACE. IN THAT SPACE IS
OUR POWER TO CHOOSE
OUR RESPONSE. IN OUR
RESPONSE LIES OUR GROWTH
AND OUR FREEDOM."

VIKTOR E. FRANKL,
*MAN'S SEARCH
FOR MEANING*

LILY PAD

Frogs don't drink water using their mouths; they absorb water through their permeable skin. In this stage, stop talking and pay attention to your body. Feel into what's going on in you.

What is your body saying to you?

It will provide data—the knot in your stomach; the fatigue you feel; the sweaty palms, your accelerated heart rate, the lump in your throat.

What's the source of that feeling?

What might it be signaling? For me, a knot in my stomach means I need to push through some discomfort and speak up about something.

"WE DON'T
LEARN FROM
EXPERIENCE. WE
LEARN BY REFLECTING
ON EXPERIENCE."
JOHN DEWEY

"NOTHING
IN LIFE IS TO BE
FEARED—IT IS TO
BE UNDERSTOOD."
MARIE CURIE

"THE CHALLENGE OF MINDFULNESS IS TO BE PRESENT FOR YOUR EXPERIENCE AS IT IS, RATHER THAN IMMEDIATELY JUMPING IN TO CHANGE IT OR TRY TO FORCE IT TO BE DIFFERENT."

JON KABAT-ZINN, PHD

LILY PAD

One of the strategies that helps us to be more resilient is reframing. Reframing is defined as the process of changing the focus of a situation or problem and examining it from a different perspective. For instance, we can reframe a rainy day as a chance to hunker down indoors and relax.

Reframing, in essence, converts problems into challenges and opportunities.

Wayne Dyer said, "Change the way you look at things, and the things you look at change."

What might you need to reframe?

<u>O</u>VERCOMING <u>O</u>BSTACLES
HAVE A HEART OPEN TO POSSIBILITY, A WILLINGNESS TO DO WHAT IT TAKES, AND A FAITH THAT IT ALL WORKS OUT.

O BSTACLES ARE A necessary part of building resilience. In this stage, you leave denial and become fully aware of the many obstacles you're facing. There may be a lot of obstacles to overcome—from physical ones to the voices in your head. The question is how do you begin to manage and overcome them?

Did you know that frogs can see forwards, sideways and upwards all at the same time? They never close their eyes, even when they sleep. However, they have eyelids that blink to protect their eyes from dirty residue and preserve their moisture. Maybe you feel somewhat like this. You feel like you can't possibly rest your eyes, you can't sleep, and you may be trying to see forward, sideways and upward, but… you just can't.

Don't fret. The way through adversity is one next move at a time. The next right move is all you need to see. The first step is to acknowledge and accept the obstacles on the road to your transformation.

In the process of overcoming obstacles, you'll experience a myriad of emotions. Some of them will be lighter emotions of hope and celebration as you overcome obstacles and feel headway. Some of your emotions will feel darker and have you feeling broken, blocked or plain old bad.

Just remember, heavy emotions are not proof of failure, just proof of your humanity. So, use these pages to dump the heaviness or celebrate your wins.

57

JUMPSTART!

Not sure where to begin? Choose a prompt from below to jump-start your O-stage writing. Find you have more to say? Open to a blank page and keep on writing.

What gray emotions are building in you that you may need to accept as part of the journey? #nobaddays isn't real. We all know that. Don't feel shame about having a bad time or difficult emotions.

....

....

....

The Dalai Llama said, *"If you think you're too small to make a difference, try sleeping with a mosquito."* Petty negative thoughts and words are like mosquitos; even the smallest ones can rob us of our peace. What negative thoughts do you need to tell to buzz off?

....

....

....

Where are you spending energy blaming or resenting? Who or what is your blame directed at? Use this opportunity to openly express that blame. Then...let it go. Resentment is like drinking poison and waiting for the other person to die. It only harms us. So, release the poison here and walk away cleansed.

....

....

....

What obstacle are you facing right now? What's one simple step you could take to meet it head on? The next move after that will become clearer.

In uncertain times, it's helpful to surround yourself with truth-tellers. These may be people who are removed from the situation and can see it objectively, or they may be people close to the situation who can shed light on something you need to see. Who are your loving truth-tellers? What are they helping you to see?

What is one of your favorite inspiring quotes? Capture it here.

Why did you choose this quote? How does it speak to you?

Ommm...The power of a good mantra can be grounding. A mantra helps you return from the past or future and be in the present. I wear a bracelet that simply says *"let it be."* The pillow in my bedroom says *"be still."* What simple phrase or mantra grounds you and provides some constant reminder that brings you back to center? It could be words to a song, some scripture, a quote. Write about your mantra , why you chose it, and how it grounds you.

....

....

....

What courage do you need to summon right now?

....

....

....

In times of change and transformation, circumstances are continually changing. Aiming for perfection is futile. In fact, perfection can be the enemy of progress. Where do you need to let go of perfection and embrace "good enough?"

....

....

....

What are your core fears about being imperfect?

....

....

....

It's easy to focus on how much further we have to go. But celebrate the progress! List 5 victories—no matter how small—that you've accomplished this week.

1. ....

2. ....

3. ....

4. ....

5. ....

Where are you already feeling some growth that's worthy of reflecting on and recording here?

....

....

....

Breathe it in…there's more growth to come.

KEEP ON WRITING...

> "COURAGE AT ITS MOST POWERFUL IS RARELY LOUD. MOSTLY IT'S A WHISPER—THOSE MOMENTS EVERY DAY WHEN YOU DO WHAT MATTERS. COURAGE IS NOT ABOUT NOT BEING FEARFUL, BUT ABOUT WALKING IN THE DIRECTION OF YOUR FEAR STEP BY STEP."
>
> SUSAN DAVID,
> EMOTIONAL AGILITY

"LIFE'S PROBLEMS WOULDN'T BE CALLED 'HURDLES' IF THERE WASN'T A WAY TO GET OVER THEM."

ANONYMOUS

"LIFE IS
NOT ALWAYS A
MATTER OF HOLDING
GOOD CARDS, BUT
SOMETIMES, PLAYING
A POOR HAND WELL."

JACK LONDON

LILY PAD

Cross Currents. As you shoulder new responsibilities and gather yourself for what's ahead, additional challenges will be put in your path. These cross currents test your resolve. They test how badly you want to make progress. However, what feels like rocks on the path could actually be weird stepping stones.

What cross currents are you experiencing? In due time, you'll see where they were leading you.

LILY PAD

Here are some strategies for dealing with life in the O stage. Which of these do you most need to work on right now? What step(s) could you take to put this strategy in place?

- **O**vertaking the Voice in your Head

- **O**vercoming Anxiety

- **O**vercoming Blame

- **O**rganizing your Tribe—when it comes to inner growth, the vast majority of us cannot grow in isolation. Who are the people who can support you?

- **O**bserving the Opportunities in front of you

KEEP ON WRITING...

> "BEING DEFEATED IS TEMPORARY. GIVING UP IS WHAT MAKES IT PERMANENT."
>
> MARILYN VOS SAVANT

"DON'T BE A
FISH; BE A FROG.
SWIM IN THE WATER
AND JUMP WHEN YOU
HIT GROUND."

YOUNG-HA KIM

"WHEN YOU MEET
OBSTACLES WITH
GRATITUDE, YOUR
PERCEPTION STARTS
TO SHIFT, RESISTANCE
LOSES ITS POWER,
AND GRACE FINDS A
HOME WITHIN YOU."

OPRAH WINFREY

LILY PAD

Need a boost? Music can raise our energetic vibration—move us from *waah* to *why not*! Like other pleasurable sensations, listening to music triggers the release of **dopamine,** a brain chemical that makes us feel engaged and motivated.

What songs are part of your overcoming obstacles playlist? List them here and then listen to your playlist often to provide a much-needed lift and some inspiration.

....

....

....

....

....

....

LILY PAD

Confusing stuff happens on the road to resilience.

- Freak out
- Breathe
- Ask yourself, "what's the next right thing to do?"
- Do it
- Keep doing the next right thing
- Notice your headway
- Celebrate how capable and calm you suddenly feel

<u>G</u>EE, I THINK I'M <u>G</u>ROWING

YOU AREN'T ALONE OR CRAZY—JUST GROWING ONE (PAINFUL) DECISION AND CHOICE AT A TIME.

TADPOLES SHED THEIR skin as they grow and change. They also quite literally have to find their legs. Tadpoles start growing hind legs within 6 weeks after birth, and their front legs soon follow. On average, it takes 20-25 weeks after birth for tadpoles to efficiently use their legs. The point is, it's a process. In this stage, you are shedding old ways and realities and watching new ones take their place. Growth takes place over time. This is a stage for acknowledging that progress.

Julia Cameron, author of *The Artist's Way* wrote:

> "**Growth** is an erratic forward movement: two steps forward and one step back. Remember that and be very gentle with yourself. You may feel capable of great things on Tuesday, but on Wednesday you may slide backward. This is normal. Growth occurs in spurts. You will lie dormant sometimes. Do not be discouraged. Think of it as resting."

Part of growth is giving up victimhood. So put down your middle finger and collect the pieces of your crumbling heart...whenever you're ready. Eventually, you'll begin to believe that whatever disorienting event triggered you, isn't happening TO you. It didn't happen because you are unworthy, being punished, stupid, or all the unflattering things that voice in your head may be saying to you. It's happening FOR you...to stimulate your growth and to create an even better, more badass, version of you.

But, our growth isn't always obvious. You need to be on the lookout for it. And others often hear and see it in us before we do. This section of the journal is a place to capture that growth that you or others see. It helps us to see the "why" behind whatever we're experiencing and acknowledge that—much like a frog—we're slowly but surely finding our legs and new ways to navigate our terrain.

JUMPSTART!

Not sure where to begin? Choose a prompt from below to jump-start your G-stage writing. Find you have more to say? Open to a blank page and keep on writing.

Grief is part of the process. Growth actually starts with mourning "what was" on the road to "what will be." What are you sad to let go of? What do you want to celebrate letting go of?

How is your new reality showing up in promising ways? Where are you seeing evidence of something even better showing up?

On average, a frog completely sheds its skin about once a week. It may shed its skin based on growth, a new environment or toxins in the environment. Describe the old skin you are shedding and how that feels.

Now describe your new skin.

....

....

....

What relationships have you outgrown or are you outgrowing?

....

....

....

What new relationships are showing up?

....

....

....

What meaning are you giving your situation or event? How *could* you look at it instead? Changing the meaning won't change the event, but how you look at it will help you to deal with it better. Friends, family, counselors, and therapists can be helpful.

....

....

....

What parts of your situation have you accepted?

....

....

....

Which parts are you still working to accept?

....

....

....

How are you growing? Where do you deserve a high five?

....

....

....

What strengths and gifts do you possess to help you on this transformation journey? This is no time to be humble. Capture them here and remind yourself of how much greatness you possess to leverage in your situation. What new strengths are surfacing and perhaps surprising you?

....

....

....

What goals and projects, that have been on hold, can you now pursue?

....

....

....

What are you feeling grateful for about your journey? List them. They could be big or small.

....

....

....

If you were asked to give a commencement speech to someone on your same journey, what would you say? What advice would you offer the grads?

....

....

....

How are you now able to show up for others in places of need with more empathy and compassion? How is your disorienting life event serving you—and others? Who are you feeling more compassion for? In what way do you feel more empathetic?

....

....

....

KEEP ON WRITING...

> "IN THE DEPTHS OF WINTER, I FINALLY LEARNED THAT WITHIN ME LAY AN INVINCIBLE SUMMER."
>
> ALBERT CAMUS

"A TREE CAN ONLY GIVE SHADE TO OTHERS AFTER IT'S GROWN ITSELF."

JAY SHETTY

"IF YOU ARE NOT A LITTLE BIT UNCOMFORTABLE EVERY DAY, YOU'RE NOT GROWING. ALL THE GOOD STUFF IS JUST OUTSIDE YOUR COMFORT ZONE."

JACK CANFIELD

LILY PAD

Activity: Label one of the blank journal pages MY FUTURE. Notice the blank piece of paper staring back at you. That's your future. It isn't written yet. You are the writer of it.

Not your past, not your losses.

You.

You are the creator of your future. Don't let your mind tell you otherwise. Don't let your past dictate your future.

What future do you most want for yourself?

Get writing!!

KEEP ON WRITING...

> "WE THINK TOO
> SMALL, LIKE THE FROG
> AT THE BOTTOM OF THE
> WELL. HE THINKS THE SKY IS
> ONLY AS BIG AS THE TOP OF
> THE WELL. IF HE SURFACED, HE
> WOULD HAVE AN ENTIRELY
> DIFFERENT VIEW."
>
> MAO TSE-TUNG

"WHEN WE
FOCUS ON OUR
GRATITUDE, THE TIDE
OF DISAPPOINTMENT
GOES OUT AND
THE TIDE OF LOVE
RUSHES IN."

KRISTIN ARMSTRONG

"ONE CAN CHOOSE
TO GO BACK TOWARD
SAFETY OR FORWARD
TOWARD GROWTH.
GROWTH MUST BE
CHOSEN AGAIN AND
AGAIN; FEAR MUST
BE OVERCOME AGAIN
AND AGAIN."

ABRAHAM MASLOW

LILY PAD

Here are some strategies and considerations for the G(rowth) space you're in. Which ones are speaking to you?

↗ **Grieve**–Growth starts with an acknowledgement that something is changing. It requires letting go of something comfortable and familiar in order for something better to show up. As we experience this loss, it's important to acknowledge and grieve your old reality.

↗ **Get To**–When you replace "I *have to*" or "I *should*" with "I *get to*" you bring a different energy to your actions. What do you *get* to do as a result of your changing situation? For example, do you *have* to spend more time alone or do you *get* to spend more time alone?

↗ **Gratitude Power:** As your transition fog lifts, you'll find more to be grateful for if you are open to it and go looking for it. Slowly finding gratitude for your situation and journey multiplies how much you have that you can be grateful for.

↗ **Get to Acceptance:** Acceptance doesn't happen all at once. Acceptance grows slowly in us. The deeper we go into acceptance, the less we need to know the *why*. The short answer for why things happen to us is *for our growth*. Where are you seeing signs of some gradual acceptance of your situation?

↗ **Giving Back (to yourself and others).** How do you want to celebrate your headway? Make time to mark your progress. How can you use your experience to give back to others? Doing so will fuel you as you find meaning in your disorienting experience. As Buddha says, "*if you are a lamp for someone else, it will brighten your path.*" Helping others will help the recipient and you.

SOVEREIGN, SIGNIFICANTLY EXPANDED SELF

BEHIND EVERY *NOW WHAT?* IS A *WHY NOT?!*
READY TO BE UNLEASHED!

THIS IS THE stage of arriving—temporarily. A space of progress on the other end of a disorienting time. Ideally, the S also stands for Self-Love for hanging in there through rough times...for letting yourself feel the unflattering, shadowy parts of yourself...for being responsible and intentional in the tough times...for all the obstacles you overcame...and the incredible growth that has led to this place. A place where your self-love score deserves a bump.

By the time you reach this stage you've not only morphed from tadpole to frog, grown legs, lost a tail, and learned to navigate water and land—you've donned a crown. Why a crown? Because you are resilience royalty!

Sovereignty is defined as "the source of eternal and unlimited power, supremacy within self, befitting of royalty." Why royalty? Because you're crowning a more royal, expanded version of yourself. That crown was not given to you by anyone else. It's there because you're earned it as a result of the disorienting life event you took on. You found your power in the midst of uncertainty.

And here's the thing—there was no magical kiss or wand involved—just you taking small, sustained steps and putting in the work to grow more resilient.

You: picking up jewels about yourself in this process.

You: a stronger, more evolved, expanded, transformed version of yourself.

You've come home to a new iteration of yourself—again. It's not the first time, and it won't be the last time. But it deserves acknowledgement!

JUMPSTART!

Not sure where to begin? Choose a prompt from below to jump-start your S-stage writing. Find you have more to say? Open to a blank page and keep on writing.

How are you seeing yourself differently?

What do you especially love about yourself right now?

What lessons have you learned on the way to crowning your royal, more expanded, sovereign self?

What can you see now that you could never have seen or known before? What new perspective has shown up?

"My crown is in my heart, not on my head; Not deck'd with diamonds and Indian stones, Nor to be seen: my crown is call'd content; A crown it is that seldom kings enjoy." William Shakespeare (1564 - 1616) As you look into your heart, in what ways are you more content than you've been for a while?

....

....

....

What deserves a celebration for getting to this new place? What do you want to pat yourself on the back about?

....

....

....

If you were able to plan a well-deserved celebration for yourself, what would it look like? A getaway? A party? A quiet acknowledgement to yourself? Plan the party or write that celebration note here.

....

....

....

None of us takes this transformation journey alone. As you reflect on yours, who would you like to thank for their role and what would you say to each of them?

....

....

....

Who have you found the strength to forgive or accept along the way?

....

....

....

Reflecting on your journey, what pleasant surprises showed up?

....

....

....

What possibilities for the future make you excited? What goals and projects have been on hold that you're ready to pursue? What new goals do you have?

....

....

....

What wisdom would you like to share with others on a similar transformation journey?

....

....

....

In what ways are you more resilient than ever?

....

....

....

KEEP ON WRITING...

"IT WASN'T A KISS THAT CHANGED THE FROG, BUT THE FACT THAT A YOUNG GIRL LOOKED BENEATH WARTS AND SLIME AND BELIEVED SHE SAW A PRINCE. SO, HE BECAME ONE."

RICHELLE E. GOODRICH,
MAKING WISHES: QUOTES,
THOUGHTS & A LITTLE
POETRY FOR EVERY
DAY OF THE YEAR

5 FROGS

"ONE DAY, IN
RETROSPECT,
THE YEARS OF
STRUGGLE WILL
STRIKE YOU AS THE
MOST BEAUTIFUL."
SIGMUND FREUD

"THE COMEBACK
IS ALWAYS
STRONGER THAN
THE SETBACK."
UNKNOWN

LILY PAD

My Story—

On the other side of my divorce, I found myself talking with others about what I wanted for my new life. I couldn't envision any specifics, but I'd consistently extend my arms palms up in front of me and then out to the sides. I had no words, just this simple gesture.

I came to know the word later: EXPANSIVE. I wanted a more expansive life. I wanted to move from a contracted state—constricted, confined, tight, locked down, to an expansive state—open, relaxed, fearless, powerful, strong. As humans, we move between these two states constantly.

But each time we leave a contracted state, we level up to an even more expansive state of possibility. As I envisioned my more expansive life, I asked myself some questions:

"What dreams have I yet to pursue?"

"What creative possibilities are out there to explore?"

"What's possible in my new situation that wasn't before?"

How do *you* see yourself or your life getting even more expansive?

KEEP ON WRITING...

> "A STRONG WOMAN
> KNOWS SHE
> HAS STRENGTH
> ENOUGH FOR THE
> JOURNEY, BUT A
> WOMAN OF STRENGTH
> KNOWS IT IS IN THE
> JOURNEY WHERE SHE
> WILL BECOME STRONG."
>
> UNKNOWN

"IT IS ONLY
POSSIBLE TO
LIVE HAPPILY EVER
AFTER ON A DAY-
TO-DAY BASIS."

M. W. BONNANO

"TO BE YOURSELF
IN A WORLD THAT
IS CONSTANTLY
TRYING TO MAKE YOU
SOMETHING ELSE,
IS THE GREATEST
ACCOMPLISHMENT."

RALPH WALDO EMERSON

LILY PAD

Selfebrate! Don't grab a dictionary. I made this word up. My definition is "to celebrate one's self and progress (no matter how big or small) on the journey of discovery, growth or transformation." The gold we seek is often hidden in the dark. If we found some gold, we'd be selfebrating big time! So, what's worthy of a selfebration, and how will you honor your headway?

Remember: what we appreciate, tends to appreciate.

LILY PAD

According to research by Brené Brown, "The most vulnerable emotion we experience as humans is not grief, fear, and shame—it's joy. Joy is the most vulnerable emotion because we are so afraid to let ourselves feel it because of its impermanence. We're afraid that if we lean into it someone may take it away, and we'll be blindsided by pain."

Where are you experiencing joy? Lean into it and capture the moment with gratitude.

HOPS

A HOP is a shorter distance than a jump or a leap. You may not be feeling like you've experienced a monumental leap at the moment, but this is a space to take note of the hops you're taking.

Take some time to reflect on earlier entries. Do this weekly or monthly. Note any observations, celebrations, new opportunities, growth, or next steps. What expansion are you witnessing in yourself? How are you transforming bit by bit?

Notice that a HOP is only one letter away from HOPE.

HOP...

HOP...

HOP...

HOP...

HOP...

HOP...

HOP...

HOP...

HOP...

HOP...

HOP...

HOP...

HOP...

HOP...

REFLECTIONS ON THE ROAD TO RESILIENCE

"LIFE'S LIKE A MOVIE. WRITE YOUR OWN ENDING."

— The Muppet Movie, 1979

WHEN "STUFF HAPPENS" and we find ourselves in some plan B, it usually feels more like it's happening *to* us than *for* us. Only with time, can we see that it was really in our best interest – that during the transition we were in, some big reshuffling of the deck was occurring. And while we may never want to go through it again, it's creating a necessary shift.

Creating this 5 FROGS® journal was just one of the "why nots" that got unleashed during my own journey. I'm happy it landed in your hands and would love to hear what your journey unleashed in you.

Feel free to reach me at BrendaKReynolds.com and to learn more about all that my journey has unleashed, and other ways you or your group can continue to be supported by my programs or services.

You aren't the same person you were when you began this journey and journal. Chances are you are already handling situations better than your old self would have. You are more resilient! And ready to handle the next transformation life calls on you to make. It's inevitable that more change will come your way, but change is full of both vague uncertainty and brilliant promise.

You've got this!

Warmly,
Brenda

125

ABOUT THE AUTHOR

B RENDA K. REYNOLDS is a trusted consultant, coach, author, and international speaker specializing in guiding individuals and client organizations through periods of uncertainty and change to foster resilience.

Having experienced a life gone sideways in 2008, Brenda continues to turn her own *"now what?"* moments into *"why nots?!"* This guided journal is her latest contribution to others experiencing life shifts.

She is author of the Amazon best seller *TBD: To Be Determined— Leading with Clarity & Confidence in Uncertain Times.* She is a TEDx speaker on *Navigating Transition Fog,* creator of *The Now What Transformation® Clarity card deck,* and originator of the 5 FROGS® framework for resilience.

Brenda also delivers compelling, inspirational keynotes, seminars and workshops focused on navigating change, leadership, and staying resilient. She lives in the Philadelphia area, where she continues on her own 5 FROGS® journey!

To learn more or contact Brenda, please visit www.BrendaKReynolds.com.

Printed in the USA
CPSIA information can be obtained
at www.ICGtesting.com
CBHW042230130324
5167CB00072BA/411